A gift for

_____

(a true woman of substance)

From

_____

Women of Substance

by Oliver Christianson, a.k.a, Revilo

Editors: Jane-Elyse Pryor and Todd Hafer
Designed by: Wale Adeniran
Production Art: Dan Horton
Art Director: Mark Cordes

Printed and Bound in China
BOK 2061

Dedicated to

Sylvia, Zoe,

and women of substance everywhere

Raves for Revilo

Revilo is a funny guy, and he is a gentle guy. These two things, plus his excellent taste in eyeglass frames, endear him to me. And what I love so much about the cartoons he pens is that they are wickedly funny without being funny at someone else's expense. That is a true gift.

–Hilary Price
Rhymes With Orange

On behalf of big girls everywhere, I challenge Revilo to a footrace around the Washington Monument.

–M.K. Brown

Oliver is one of those men with the rare ability to reach down into the depths of the female psyche and push the buttons that make us laugh at ourselves. I'm not sure what that says about him, but his cartoons are funny.

–Sandra Bell-Lundy
Between Friends

Never mind The Swan–thanks to Oliver, I've got substance!

–Patricia Storms

Oliver is a highly evolved cartoonist: funnier than most – but not as hairy.

–Teresa Dowlatshahi
Shoecabbage

Revilo is my very favorite "man who must have been a woman in a former life" cartoonist. He really gets us. Or his wife really gets us and fills him in. Either way, he has a wonderfully original mind, and his stuff is very, very funny. I've sent out hundreds of his cards. Really.

–Jan Eliot
Stone Soup

Is Revilo sexist or does he just draw the funniest cartoons about women since God designed Adam? I took a poll of super-heroines, hula girls, girl reporters, prom queens, chunky women in bathing suits with ruffles on the bottom, and New York senators named Hilary, and they all agreed: funny. Then, just to make sure, I asked God, and She said so, too.

–Trina Robbins
Author of Eternally Bad: Goddesses with Attitude,
Tender Murderers: Women Who Kill, and Wild Irish Roses.

Oliver's cartoons make me feel pretty.

–Renee Andriani
Shoebox Cards artist

Hallmark has asked me to say a few words about my philosophy.

I draw cartoons.

MOTHERHOOD 101

MOTHERHOOD
ONE MILLION B.C.

ONE MOTHER'S FANTASY:

SECRET DOORS WITH HIDDEN PASSAGEWAYS FOR ESCAPING THE FAMILY.

SOME MOTHERS ARE COMPULSIVE CLEANERS.

WHEN GOOD MOMS GO BAD

MOTHER ON THE EDGE

REViLo

Some mothers end up
carrying their babies
a whole lot longer
than nine months.

The Scream-Your-Guts-Out Lecture.

Q. Malls are a good place to meet men.

True or False ?

Example #1

Example #2

Example #3

Example #4

Example #5

Example #6

REViLo

THIS OUTFIT LOOKED SO CUTE IN THE CATALOG.

HE SAID, SHE SAID

Startling proof that men CAN dance.

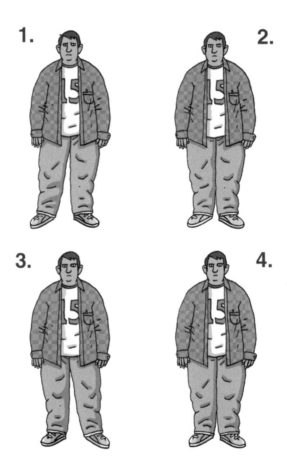

WEDDINGS

THE BRIDE OF TERROR

MRS. I-LET-SOME-ONE-IN-MY-FAMILY-DO-MY-HAIR.

MRS. LARGE

MRS. PERKY

MRS. GOONPIE

MRS. SECOND THOUGHTS

MRS. SKINHEAD

MRS. HAIR

MRS. TIGHTLY WOUND

MRS. NO NECK

REVILO

A story with a happy ending.

1. BOY MEETS GIRL.

2. BOY ROMANCES GIRL.

3. BOY BEGINS ACTING LIKE A JERK.

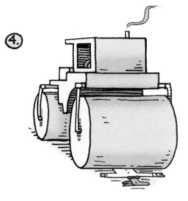

4. GIRL RUNS DOWN BOY WITH STEAMROLLER.

REViLo

I SKYDIVE TO RELAX.
FOR SHEER TERROR, I DATE.

Women are the truth tellers in our society.

THE REAL PRINCE CHARMING

That sunless tanning lotion
seems to work best
on the palms of my hands.

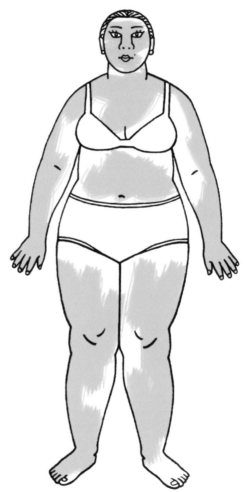

REVILO

all men are hot.

Just ask them!

REVILO

When it comes to breaking up,
honesty is not always the best policy.

ICE CREAM AND ROMANCE

SOME THINGS JUST NATURALLY GO TOGETHER!

REVILO

It's a little-known fact that if you add enough fruit to cheesecake, it's no longer considered a dessert.

It's true, really!

REViLo

COMMON FIGURE FLAWS

  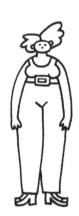 

BIG HIPS   LONG WAIST,   SHORT WAIST,   POORLY DRAWN
            SHORT LEGS   LONG LEGS   HEAD

PENCILS ALFREDO

Very low in carbs.

REVILO

EXTREME MAKE-OVERS!

462:
Lot's Wife

BEFORE   AFTER

STUPID THINGS AEROBICS
INSTRUCTORS SAY #87:

The "I'm pretending I'm on a diet" Salad.

What your ponytail says about you!

If you wear your hair pulled back, it means you're quiet and studious.

If you wear your hair pulled to the left, it means that you're the creative type.

If you wear your hair pulled to the right, it means you're thrifty and practical.

If you wear all of your hair pulled to the front, it means you won't be able to see where you're going.

REVILO

THE DO-IT-YOURSELF FACE LIFT.

NOTE: This procedure is covered by virtually all company medical plans.

SOME DAYS, I'M LUCKY iF I CAN
EVEN DO THE SEMi-BLOATUS POSiTiON.

I LIKE HAIRSTYLES THAT
MAKE IT HARD TO TELL WHEN
I'M HAVING A BAD HAIR DAY.

WEDDINGS

MRS. BLAH   MRS. DIZZY   MRS. PANIC   MRS. FOREHEAD   MRS. TIPSY

MRS. PSYCHO   MRS. TOOTH   MRS. CRANIAL DEVICE   MRS. EVIL EYE   MRS. CHINFIST

I'M WAITING TO BE DISCOVERED
BY ONE OF THOSE TV SHOWS
WHERE THEY HAVE A BUNCH OF
ATTRACTIVE GUYS BREAK INTO
MY HOUSE AND GIVE ME A MAKE-OVER.

PAREOS USED TO BE CALLED
"COVER-UPS" TiLL WOMEN
DiSCOVERED THEY REALLY
DiDN'T COVER ANYTHiNG UP.

HERE SHE IS...

...the only woman I know of who really does have firm thighs.

USEFUL ADVICE:

NEVER MARRY ANYONE YOU MEET
PLAYING THE SLOTS AT 3 A.M.
IN LAS VEGAS.

I THINK
BALLET IS 99% ATTITUDE,
DON'T YOU?

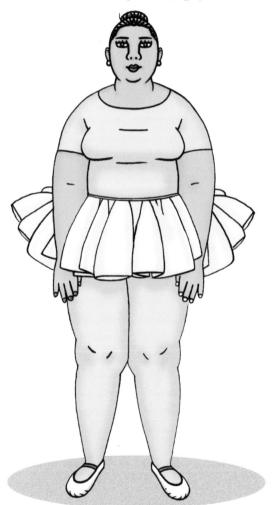

Ladies,
don't you just hate it when
the door to your igloo shrinks
during the winter?

From watching TV chefs, I've learned that any dish can be improved if you add lots of wine to it.

IF HOUSEPLANTS COULD HIRE
A LAWYER, I'D BE UP FOR
FIRST-DEGREE MURDER!

BROCCOLi SHARES iTS
CONCERNS ABOUT THE FUTURE.

WEDDINGS

MRS. BEANS   MRS. DULL   MRS. OILY FACE   MRS. MALL HAIR

MRS. SNOTTY   MRS. BARKING MAD   MRS. POP EYE   MRS. CLUE FREE

REVILO

WALTER FOUND OUT TOO LATE
THAT HELEN'S SECRET FANTASY
HAD NOTHING TO DO WITH SEX.

PLACES HUSBANDS DISAPPEAR #32:

Most women don't realize that
they're marrying clowns until long
after the ceremony is over.

REVILO

At Home With the Draculas

HOW COME BRA STRAPS
AREN'T CONSIDERED
A FASHION ACCESSORY?

I LOVE DRAWSTRING PANTS.
YOU CAN HIDE ANYTHING
IN THEM.

May you always be able to wear the shoes that are in fashion.

— Ancient Aztec Salutation

REViLo

Ever ask yourself,
How hard could it be
to make my own clothes?

WE'RE NOT GETTING OLDER,
WE'RE GETTING LOUDER!

ANYTHING YOU CAN WRIGGLE INTO STILL FITS.

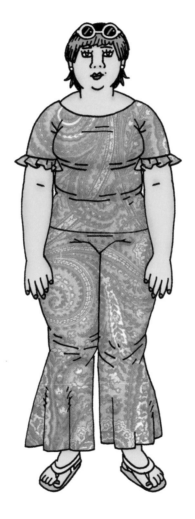

Hair
Styles
for
Shy
Women

#43

REVILO

SOMETIMES I CAN'T TELL IF I'M
"KEEPING IT REAL" OR NOT.

The Do

Make your "high style" wigs at home using industrial mops, starch, and food coloring!

Did you know
that you can guess
a person's age
by looking at their
shoes?

How sad is that?

Fashion Faux Pas # 378

Being on vacation and/or tipsy is no excuse.

Homemade Prom Dresses # 73

THE "CARGO" GIRDLE

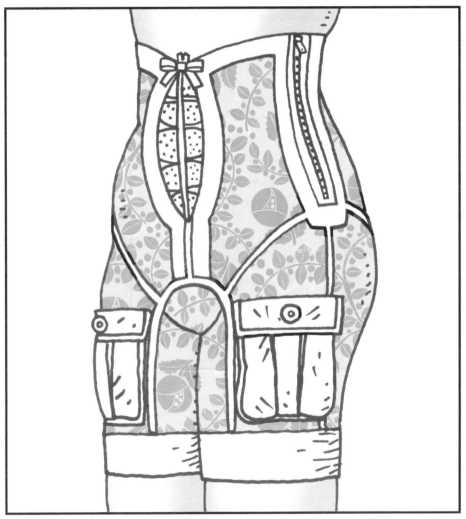

REVILO

If you talk to your plants,
they'll tell you things as well.

Available NOW where fine IMAGINARY PRODUCTS are sold!

MADELINE AT 40

Tips for Removing Heads of Fashion Dolls

Heat neck with a hair dryer - twist and POP!

REViLo

ALICE IN LUMBERLAND

How come they don't
sell coffee in my size?

If you are a woman of substance,
or just someone who likes Revilo's work,
we'd like to know what you think of this collection...
Please send your comments to:
Book Feedback
2501 McGee, Mail Drop 250
Kansas City, MO 64141-6580

Or e-mail us at

booknotes@hallmark.com

PS: If you have any messages of substance for Revilo,
include those, too, and we'll pass them along.